GLENCOE
LITERATURE
The Reader's Choice

Writing Assessment
and
Portfolio Management

Course 4

 Glencoe
McGraw-Hill

New York, New York   Columbus, Ohio   Woodland Hills, California   Peoria, Illinois

Glencoe/McGraw-Hill

A Division of The **McGraw·Hill** *Companies*

Send all inquiries to:
Glencoe/McGraw-Hill
8787 Orion Place
Columbus, Ohio 43240-4027

ISBN 0-07-826577-0

Printed in the United States of America

2 3 4 5 6 7 8 9 10   079   06 05 04 03 02

TABLE OF CONTENTS

OVERVIEW OF ASSESSMENT

The literature anthology for Grade 9 is organized by unit and theme. Each theme offers a number of Responding to Literature tasks, two Theme Projects, and a Writing Workshop that focuses on a specific kind of writing. Each of these features provides opportunities for assessment.

The purpose of any type of assessment is to measure the effectiveness of instruction and ultimately to improve or maximize instruction for each student. Assessment tools for *Glencoe Literature* support the belief that the most effective way to assess students is to use a variety of approaches and procedures: formal tests, informal assessments, writing assessments, performance assessments, and portfolios.

Assessment should be viewed as part of the teaching and learning process, not as the final step. Assessment can be used to provide feedback to students, to help them improve their work, and to help set goals for both you and your students to further instruction.

In-Text Assessments

The literature anthology for each grade provides tasks for Responding to Literature, Theme Projects, and Writing Workshops. All three kinds of tasks can be used as part of the assessment program. For example, following each selection in the anthology is a set of Responding to Literature activities, which include Personal Response, Analyzing Literature, Literature and Writing, and Extending Your Response. These activities, which provide a varied set of tasks for students to complete, may be used to help assess students' understanding of the selection and their ability to apply concepts learned from the selection in various other contexts.

Assessment Options

To supplement the In-Text Assessments, *Glencoe Literature* provides three separate assessment tools: the *Selection and Theme Assessment* book, *Performance Assessments,* and *Writing Assessment and Portfolio Management.* Each assessment tool has a different purpose and elicits a different kind of information, as described below.

- The **Selection and Theme Assessment** book includes tests for all selections and a test for each theme. The Selection Tests are formal one- or two-page tests designed to assess students' comprehension of the selections. Each test has up to four parts—Recalling and Interpreting, Using Vocabulary, Interpreting and Evaluating, and Evaluating and Connecting—which include multiple-choice questions, graphic organizers, and essay questions. The Open-Book Theme Test is a two-page assessment designed to evaluate students' understanding of all the selections in the theme. Students are asked to apply what they have learned as they compare and contrast selections in the theme.

- The ***Performance Assessments*** book provides assessments for each literature selection and the two Theme Projects for each theme. The task or activity the book provides for each selection may be used as an alternative, or as a supplement, to the formal Selection Test. The book also provides a framework for using the Theme Projects as alternatives or supplements to the Theme Tests.

- The ***Writing Assessment and Portfolio Management*** book provides information, criteria, rubrics, and forms that both teachers and students can use to assess writing and to manage and evaluate portfolios. The purpose of this book is threefold: (1) to provide general information and rubrics for evaluating students' writing, (2) to provide specific information and rubrics for the individual Writing Workshop activities in the anthology, and (3) to provide guidelines and support for managing and evaluating portfolios.

With this wide array of assessment tools available, you may want to use a number of approaches to assess and evaluate students' work. For example, to supplement the In-Text Assessments in the anthology, you might use Selection Tests to assess students' understanding of the literature selections in one theme. In other themes, you might use *Performance Assessments* to assess students' abilities to apply their understanding of the selection in various media or contexts. Or, you might use different assessments for students with different learning styles: some students may respond better to formal multiple-choice tests, while others may respond better to more open-ended kinds of projects or activities. There are assessments that will engage the visual, audio/verbal, and kinesthetic learners. Talent, learning style, and variety of presentation are all taken into account in the *Performance Assessments.*

Writing Assessment and Portfolio Management

PART ONE: **WRITING ASSESSMENT**

This section provides

- strategies for effective assessment.

- methods of writing assessment.

- general guidelines, forms, and rubrics for different methods of writing assessment.

- specific rubrics and models for each of the student anthology's Writing Workshop activities.

Please note that although the Writing Workshops, which are located at the end of each theme, instruct students about specific types of writing, the rubrics presented for the resulting compositions can also be used to assess the performance of students on other types of writing.

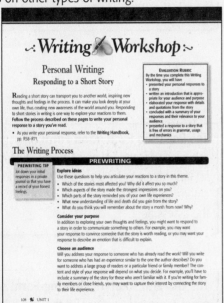

Writing Assessment and Portfolio Management

Strategies for Effective Writing Assessment

Assessments may be conducted for many purposes, but the ultimate goal is always to improve instruction for each student. Whatever method of assessment you use, consider the following strategies for making your assessment as effective as possible.

- **Make sure students know the criteria for good writing.** We can expect students to produce good writing only if they understand what good writing is. For example, a student writing a personal essay needs to know that personal essays express the writer's thoughts and opinions, they often incorporate personal anecdotes or experiences, and they are usually written in a less formal style than a literary analysis or other form of essay. In an assessment situation, it is only fair for students to know how their work will be judged. Knowing the criteria for good writing will also help students evaluate and revise their own writing before it is submitted for teacher evaluation. When you give students the criteria, discuss what is expected of them.

> When students are working on a particular type of writing, you may want to distribute copies of an appropriate **rubric,** pages 14–49, so that students can continually refer to the criteria listed there as they compose and revise.

- **Let students help develop the criteria.** If it is feasible in your classroom, have students get involved in determining the criteria you and they will use for evaluating a piece of writing. This will give students a sense of ownership and will help them to see why a given piece of writing does or does not meet the criteria.

> The **Portfolio Evaluation Form** on page 60 provides space to list any criteria developed by individuals or by the class so that those criteria might be taken into account during the assessment.

- **Evaluate the writing process, not just the final product.** Writing is a process of steps, from the idea to the finished manuscript. Students will improve their writing as they increase their ability to complete each step in the process. An assessment of student writing that includes review and discussion of each step will help students understand what works in their writing and why it works.

> The **General Analytic Scoring Form** on page 10 provides a checklist that can help you review and discuss each step of the writing process with students.

Writing Assessment and Portfolio Management

- **Explain to students how their writing will be scored.** Students should know how you will be scoring their work and how to interpret the scores. For example, a student who receives a 3 on a composition should know what the score means and on what criteria it was based.

- **Provide opportunities for feedback.** Whenever possible, give students feedback about their writing to help them understand their strengths and weaknesses and identify what parts or aspects of their writing need to be improved. Providing frequent feedback can also be valuable in helping to identify patterns of growth, providing direction for a student's individual development, and helping students improve their abilities to assess their own work and respond to the writing of others. Feedback may be provided in writing or in conversation during a conference with the student. Different kinds of feedback may also be provided through peer assessment.

- **Encourage self- and peer assessment.** Students can develop a clear sense of their abilities by evaluating their own writing. For example, you might have students evaluate their own works, assign their own scores, and write brief notes explaining why they think their scores are accurate. Then, after you score each paper, you and the student can discuss why your scores might differ. Peer assessment can also be a valuable tool throughout the writing process. Students can discuss their ideas with their partners, and partners can act as the audience during each stage of the writing.

> The **Self-Assessment Guide** on page 12 can help students evaluate themselves, and the **Peer Response Guide** on page 11 can help students evaluate each other.

Writing Assessment and Portfolio Management

Methods for Evaluating Student Writing

To help you evaluate students' writing in the *Glencoe Literature* program, this book provides guidelines for

- **formal evaluation,** including holistic, primary trait, and analytic methods
- **informal evaluation**
- **portfolio evaluation**

As you plan and administer your approach to writing assessment, keep in mind that you may want to use a variety of scoring methods or a combination of the methods described here for different writing tasks and different purposes. For example, holistic scoring is an efficient means of scoring a large number of papers quickly, but it does not provide detailed feedback for the writer. Analytic scoring provides detailed feedback to help the student improve his or her writing, but it takes considerably longer than does holistic scoring.

Formal Evaluation

- **Holistic scoring** is a quick method of evaluating a composition based on the reader's general impression of the overall quality of the writing–you can generally read a student's composition and assign a score to it in two or three minutes. Holistic scoring is usually based on a scale of 0–4, 0–5, or 0–6. Scoring criteria may consist of general guidelines for each score point. Or, they may focus on specific characteristics of a type of writing that you should keep in mind as you read to gain a general impression of the student's work.

    To score students' writing based on general guidelines, refer to the **General Rubric for Holistic Scoring** on pages 8–9. The criteria on this rubric can generally be applied to academic writing. When you score each paper, keep these levels of scoring in mind, read through the paper, and assign a score of 0, 1, 2, 3, or 4. If you have a large number of papers to evaluate, or if you are working with one or more other

teachers to complete the scoring, you may want to discuss your rankings of papers by each of the four categories and choose "anchor" papers to represent each scoring level. Comparing each student's paper to the range of scores represented by anchor papers can help readers to score more consistently.

General Rubric for Holistic Scoring

Score	4 A paper in this category shows a superior command of the tools of language. It exhibits some or all of the following characteristics:	3 A paper in this category shows an adequate command of the tools of language. It exhibits some or all of the following characteristics:	2 A paper in this category shows a less than adequate command of the tools of language. It exhibits some or all of the following characteristics:	1 A paper in this category shows a consistent pattern of weakness in using the tools of language. It exhibits some or all of the following characteristics:	A **0** paper is a paper that is not scorable because
Focus and Organization	• responds to the prompt • appropriate to the audience • single, distinct focus • generally well-developed ideas or narrative • logical flow of ideas or events • opening that draws in reader; effective closing • sense of completeness	• responds to the prompt • appropriate to the audience • focus not clear at every point • some main points under-developed • ideas may not be in the most effective order • an opening, but not necessarily focused or attention-getting; attempt at a closing • sense of completeness	• responds partially to the prompt but is off-target in some way • may not show evidence of attentiveness to audience • focus on topic not consistently sustained • some lack of distinction between main ideas and details • order of ideas not effective • may be no opening sentence; no attention to closing • piece seems incomplete	• evidence of attempt to respond to prompt • no evidence of attentiveness to audience • focus on topic not sustained • no opening or closing • piece is not complete	• it does not respond to the type of writing the prompt is intended to elicit. • it cannot be read because it is illegible. • it consists of lists, notes, or drawings rather than sentences and paragraphs. • the amount of writing is too minimal to be evaluated.
Support and Evaluation	• each main idea supported by details/narrative brought to life by details • all details related to topic • choice of details effective • ideas/events related by effective transition words and phrases • varied sentence style • precise, interesting, and vivid word choice	• each main idea supported by details, but details in some paragraphs may be sketchy/narrative details sufficient to flesh out events • all details related to topic • some details not used effectively • transitions used • varied sentence style • word choice adequate to convey meaning; some precise, vivid words	• uneven development/narrative details sketchy • details may appear to be listed rather than integrated into coherent flow • some details are irrelevant • few or no transitions • most sentences simple; overall style choppy • word choice adequate to convey meaning but few precise or vivid words	• half or more of main ideas not supported by details • half or more details may be irrelevant • no transitions • sentence style choppy • vocabulary limited	
Grammar, Usage, and Mechanics	• sophisticated and consistent command of Standard English • free of spelling, capitalization, and usage errors • precise syntax; competence in coordination and subordination • few, if any, errors in punctuation	• number and type of errors not sufficient to interfere with meaning • consistent command of Standard English • few, if any, spelling, capitalization, or usage errors • competence in coordination and subordination	• number and type of errors may interfere with meaning at some points • weaknesses in command of Standard English • some spelling, capitalization, or usage errors • some fragments or run-ons • some errors in punctuation	• number and type of errors obscure meaning • inadequate grasp of Standard English • frequent errors in spelling, capitalization, and usage • many run-ons or fragments • serious and frequent punctuation errors	

8 Course 4   Writing Assessment   Writing Assessment   Course 4 9

Writing Assessment and Portfolio Management

- **Primary trait scoring,** which is also known as **focused holistic scoring,** is similar to holistic scoring, but it focuses on the most important characteristics of specific types of writing. This type of holistic scoring takes into account the differences between, for example, descriptive writing and persuasive writing. To use this approach, review the rubric for the type of writing in question before you begin scoring, and keep the criteria listed on the rubric in mind as you read and score each paper on the scale of 0–4. Specific rubrics for each Writing Workshop can be found on pages 14–49. (Although these rubrics are designed to facilitate analytic scoring, the criteria listed on them can be used in primary trait scoring also.)

- **Analytic scoring** is based on an in-depth analysis of aspects of writing such as focus/organization, elaboration/support, and conventions of grammar, usage, and mechanics. Analytic scoring is usually based on a scale of 0–100 with each aspect receiving a portion of the total points. The **General Analytic Scoring Form** on page 10 can be used to score a piece of writing in this way. Various characteristics are listed under each aspect, forming categories, and each category is assigned a weighted score. Regardless of the number of characteristics in any particular category, the weight of the category stays the same. For example, analytic scoring based on a possible total of 100 points might be weighted in this way:

Focus and Organization	35 points
Elaboration and Support	35 points
Grammar, Usage, and Mechanics	30 points

To score papers by this method, decide on the aspects and characteristics you will use and the number of points you want to assign to each category. Then read through each paper and assign a score for each category. The three (or more) scores will add up to a total score (e.g., 80 out of 100). Specific rubrics and models for each Writing Workshop can be found on pages 14–50.

Name _____ Date _____ Class _____

Writing Assessment and Portfolio Management

Rubric

Personal Writing: Responding to a Short Story (Theme 1, pages 108–112)

Focus/Organization	Comments
• Includes an introductory paragraph that identifies the title and author of the story • Provides a brief summary of the story • Focuses on personal responses to the story • Summarizes responses in a conclusion	Score _____

Elaboration/Support	Comments
• Gives reasons for personal responses • Uses quotations and details from the story to support personal responses	Score _____

Grammar, Usage, and Mechanics	Comments
• The response is free of misspellings. • Words are capitalized correctly. • Sentences are punctuated correctly, and the piece is free of fragments and run-ons. • Standard English usage is employed. • The paper is neat, legible, and presented in an appropriate format.	Score _____

Engagement in the Writing Process	Comments
The student ❑ made a prewriting plan. ❑ discussed the draft with a partner. ❑ contributed questions and suggestions to other writers. ❑ revised the draft. ❑ proofread the final draft.	Overall Score _____

14   Course 4, Theme 1   Writing Assessment

Writing Assessment and Portfolio Management

Informal Evaluation

In addition to these formal methods, **informal evaluation** of writing through observation, description, and record keeping can provide valuable information. This approach involves working closely with students, giving and receiving feedback, and adjusting instruction based on students' needs and learning goals. Unlike formal scoring of written compositions, an informal approach to evaluating students' writing can allow you to view writing as a social process and not simply a demonstration of knowledge. When you view writing as a social process, you can include students in assessment activities as readers, speakers, and listeners who are fully capable of contributing ideas, responding in an informed way, and offering suggestions.

Portfolio evaluation provides a way to combine both formal and informal methods of evaluating students' writing. There are many ways to define a portfolio, depending on individual situations. For example, some portfolios are designed as management tools for works-in-progress, some are designed as collections of best works, and others are designed as representative samples of a student's efforts. Various forms of portfolios can all provide the same or similar benefits for students.

In general, a portfolio is based on a collection of student works chosen by the student and by the teacher. Portfolios can be extremely valuable tools for encouraging students to evaluate their own work, providing an opportunity for teachers to look at strengths and weaknesses in a student's wide-ranging body of work over a period of time, and providing a means for both teachers and students to judge progress based on the concept of writing as a process. The **Portfolio Evaluation Form** on page 60 can help you and your students evaluate portfolios.

Name _____ Date _____ Class _____

Writing Assessment and Portfolio Management

Portfolio Evaluation Form

Directions: Review the contents of the portfolio and assign a rating on a scale of 1–4, where 1 indicates a need for improvement and 4 indicates excellence. In the spaces provided add any other criteria you wish to consider.

The portfolio:	Needs Improvement			Excellent
1. meets the intended purpose	1	2	3	4
2. is complete and meets all requirements	1	2	3	4
3. is well-organized	1	2	3	4
4. includes a variety of pieces	1	2	3	4
5. demonstrates concerted effort	1	2	3	4
6. illustrates appropriate level of quality	1	2	3	4
7. shows imagination and creativity	1	2	3	4
8. goes beyond minimum expectations	1	2	3	4
9. shows improvement	1	2	3	4
10. shows evidence of personal reflection and awareness of personal strengths and weaknesses	1	2	3	4

Additional Criteria

11. _____	1	2	3	4
12. _____	1	2	3	4
13. _____	1	2	3	4
14. _____	1	2	3	4

Comments and Suggestions

Copyright © by The McGraw-Hill Companies, Inc.

60   Course 4   Portfolio Management

Writing Assessment and Portfolio Management

General Rubrics and Evaluation Guides

The next few pages contain the following rubrics and forms:

- **General Rubric for Holistic Scoring**—This rubric appears on pages 8–9. It is intended for you to use to evaluate any kind of writing on a scale of 1–4. You may also want to duplicate this rubric and distribute it to students so that they understand the criteria upon which their writing will be evaluated.

- **General Analytic Scoring Form**—This form appears on page 10. It is intended for you to use to evaluate any kind of writing on a scale of 1–100. You may also want to duplicate it and distribute it to students so that they understand the criteria upon which their writing will be evaluated.

- **Peer Response Guide**—This form appears on page 11. You may use it to evaluate students' writing or you may want to duplicate it and distribute it to students so that they can help evaluate each other's writing.

- **Self-Assessment Guide**—This form appears on page 12. You may want to duplicate it and distribute it to students so that they can evaluate their own writing.

General Rubric for Holistic Scoring

Score	4	3
	A paper in this category shows a superior command of the tools of language. It exhibits some or all of the following characteristics:	A paper in this category shows an adequate command of the tools of language. It exhibits some or all of the following characteristics:
Focus and Organization	• responds to the prompt • appropriate to the audience • single, distinct focus • generally well-developed ideas or narrative • logical flow of ideas or events • opening that draws in reader; effective closing • sense of completeness	• responds to the prompt • appropriate to the audience • focus not clear at every point • some main points under-developed • ideas may not be in the most effective order • an opening, but not necessarily focused or attention-getting; attempt at a closing • sense of completeness
Support and Evaluation	• each main idea supported by details/narrative brought to life by details • all details related to topic • choice of details effective • ideas/events related by effective transition words and phrases • varied sentence style • precise, interesting, and vivid word choice	• each main idea supported by details, but details in some paragraphs may be sketchy/narrative details sufficient to flesh out events • all details related to topic • some details not used effectively • transitions used • varied sentence style • word choice adequate to convey meaning; some precise, vivid words
Grammar, Usage, and Mechanics	• sophisticated and consistent command of Standard English • free of spelling, capitalization, and usage errors • precise syntax; competence in coordination and subordination • few, if any, errors in punctuation	• number and type of errors not sufficient to interfere with meaning • consistent command of Standard English • few, if any, spelling, capitalization, or usage errors • competence in coordination and subordination

2	1	
A paper in this category shows a less than adequate command of the tools of language. It exhibits some or all of the following characteristics:	A paper in this category shows a consistent pattern of weakness in using the tools of language. It exhibits some or all of the following characteristics:	A **0** paper is a paper that is not scorable because
• responds partially to the prompt but is off-target in some way • may not show evidence of attentiveness to audience • focus on topic not consistently sustained • some lack of distinction between main ideas and details • order of ideas not effective • may be no opening sentence; no attention to closing • piece seems incomplete	• evidence of attempt to respond to prompt • no evidence of attentiveness to audience • focus on topic not sustained • no opening or closing • piece is not complete	• it does not respond to the type of writing the prompt is intended to elicit. • it cannot be read because it is illegible. • it consists of lists, notes, or drawings rather than sentences and paragraphs. • the amount of writing is too minimal to be evaluated.
• uneven development/narrative details sketchy • details may appear to be listed rather than integrated into coherent flow • some details are irrelevant • few or no transitions • most sentences simple; overall style choppy • word choice adequate to convey meaning but few precise or vivid words	• half or more of main ideas not supported by details • half or more details may be irrelevant • no transitions • sentence style choppy • vocabulary limited	
• number and type of errors may interfere with meaning at some points • weaknesses in command of Standard English • some spelling, capitalization, or usage errors • some fragments or run-ons • some errors in punctuation	• number and type of errors obscure meaning • inadequate grasp of Standard English • frequent errors in spelling, capitalization, and usage • many run-ons or fragments • serious and frequent punctuation errors	

Writing Assessment and Portfolio Management

General Analytic Scoring Form

This form may be used to score a piece of writing in relation to specific characteristics.

Focus/Organization • The main idea or story sequence is clear. • The piece fulfills its purpose and is appropriate to its intended audience. • Ideas or events are presented in an effective order. • The writing has unity and coherence.	**Comments** *Score* _____
Elaboration/Support • The opening engages the reader's attention. • All details are clearly related to the topic. • Details are sufficient and appropriate. • Word choice enhances the writing. • Effective transition words are used.	**Comments** *Score* _____
Grammar, Usage, and Mechanics • Words are spelled correctly. • Capitalization is used correctly. • Sentences are punctuated correctly, and the piece is free of fragments and run-ons. • Standard English usage is employed. • The paper is neat, legible, and presented in an appropriate format.	**Comments** *Score* _____

Engagement in the Writing Process   **Comments**

The student
❏ made a prewriting plan.
❏ discussed the draft with a partner.
❏ contributed questions and suggestions to other writers.
❏ revised the draft.
❏ proofread the final draft.

Overall Score _____

Writing Assessment and Portfolio Management

Peer Response Guide

Use this form as you respond to the writing of a classmate.

What is best about this piece of writing?

Is the opening interesting and attention-getting? What, if anything, could help make it more so?

What is the focus of this piece? Do all of the parts work to support the whole?

Would it be possible to order the ideas or events more clearly? How?

Are the paragraphs and sentences clearly and logically connected? Where could transitions be introduced to make connections more clearly?

Has the writer told enough about each part of the subject? Where are more details needed?

Where is the language precise and vivid? Where is the language vague or confusing?

Where are there errors in usage, spelling, capitalization, or punctuation that need to be corrected?

Writing Assessment and Portfolio Management

Self-Assessment Guide

Use this form to evaluate your own writing by completing each sentence below.

What I like best about this piece of writing is

When I look back at the project, the part I most enjoyed working on was

The most difficult part of the project was

I was most successful at

One thing I learned from this project is

I would assess my work on this project as (outstanding, good, fair, weak)

One thing I need to improve in my next writing project is

One goal I would like to focus on in the future is

Writing Assessment and Portfolio Management

Rubrics and Models for Writing Workshop Assignments

The following pages contain rubrics specifying what to look for in the type of writing required for each Writing Workshop, Themes 1–12. The rubrics are organized here to facilitate Analytic Scoring on a scale of 1–100, with a possible 35 points in the category of Focus/Organization, a possible 35 points in the category of Elaboration/Support, and a possible 30 points in the category of Grammar, Usage, and Mechanics.

Following each rubric is a model that represents a highly proficient student's completion of the Writing Workshop assignment. Each model includes notes to point out how the writing meets various elements of the rubric's criteria.

You may want to duplicate and distribute the rubrics to students as they enter the revising stage of their writing process, so that they understand the criteria upon which their work will be evaluated.

Writing Assessment and Portfolio Management

Rubric

Personal Writing: Responding to a Short Story (Theme 1, pages 108–112)

Focus/Organization • Includes an introductory paragraph that identifies the title and author of the story • Provides a brief summary of the story • Focuses on personal responses to the story • Summarizes responses in a conclusion	**Comments** *Score* _____
Elaboration/Support • Gives reasons for personal responses • Uses quotations and details from the story to support personal responses	**Comments** *Score* _____
Grammar, Usage, and Mechanics • The response is free of misspellings. • Words are capitalized correctly. • Sentences are punctuated correctly, and the piece is free of fragments and run-ons. • Standard English usage is employed. • The paper is neat, legible, and presented in an appropriate format.	**Comments** *Score* _____

Engagement in the Writing Process   **Comments**

The student

❑ made a prewriting plan.

❑ discussed the draft with a partner.

❑ contributed questions and suggestions to other writers.

❑ revised the draft.

❑ proofread the final draft.

Overall Score _____

Writing Assessment and Portfolio Management

Writing Model

Personal Writing: Response to a Short Story (Theme 1, pages 108–112)

Assignment: Write a personal response to a story you've read.

My Response to "The Leap"

"The Leap," by Louise Erdrich, is about a remarkable woman who risks her life to save her daughter. The mother has lost her eyesight as a result of cataracts, but even without sight her life is a reflection of precise vision and courage. Her dexterity and skill achieved as a young trapeze artist saved a life not once, but twice. Reading this story left me stunned by her courage and physical skill, and it convinced me that even when you are terrified, you can and do make life-and-death decisions.

Identifies title and author and provides a brief summary of the story

I can only imagine how the narrator's mother must have felt to lose the man she loved and the father of her unborn baby girl. I could feel the love and trust these two people shared. They were "like two sparkling birds" passing each other so high in the air, pausing and kissing "as they swooped past one another" during their trapeze act. When the storm struck and lightning destroyed the main pole of the circus tent, they began to fall to their death. This woman made a split-second decision not to cling to the man she loved, but to save herself and the child growing within her. She "changed direction" in midair, and her husband fell to his death.

Describes the writer's overall response to the story

Uses details and quotations from the story to support the writer's response

The baby did not survive, but as the story continued, I became even more amazed by this courageous woman. Although talented and competent on the trapeze, she was illiterate. She was taught to read by her future husband during her recovery in the hospital. Books became a constant part of her life, and I found it tragic that life could be so unkind as to leave her without sight in the end. Yet, I somehow think she always had enough inner strength to handle whatever she encountered.

Writing Assessment and Portfolio Management

The mother remarried and had a daughter. Reading about how she saved her daughter from the fire in their home, when rescue seemed hopeless, left me with a feeling of awe. I couldn't believe it was possible to do something this brave. I was struck by how she took control of the situation. With no time to think about the consequences, this woman acted because it was necessary to save the life of her child. She climbed out on a tree branch near her daughter's window and jumped—flew—into the child's room. I could almost hear the tree branch as it broke, "so that it cracked in her hands, cracked louder than the flames as she vaulted with it toward the edge. . . ."

The story ends with a sentence that I needed to think about: "As you fall there is time to think." I guess there will be times in my life when I will have to make such quick, critical decisions. I just hope I will have as much strength and courage as the woman in this story when I need it most.

Uses new paragraphs to introduce new ideas

Discusses the writer's personal response to the story

Concludes by comparing the writer to a character in the story

Writing Assessment and Portfolio Management

Rubric

Descriptive Writing: Character Study (Theme 2, pages 192–196)

Focus/Organization • Identifies the main impressions of the character • Describes the character's behaviors, thoughts, feelings, and physical features	**Comments** *Score* _____
Elaboration/Support • Describes scenes or incidents that reveal the character and support the main impressions • Uses dialogue, description, and anecdotes to reveal the character's personality • Uses effective language, such as vivid verbs and adjectives, to make the character come alive	**Comments** *Score* _____
Grammar, Usage, and Mechanics • The piece is free of misspellings. • Words are capitalized correctly. • Sentences are punctuated correctly, and the piece is free of fragments and run-ons. • Standard English usage is employed. • The paper is neat and legible.	**Comments** *Score* _____

Engagement in the Writing Process   **Comments**

The student
❑ made a prewriting plan.
❑ discussed the draft with a partner.
❑ contributed questions and suggestions to other writers.
❑ revised the draft.
❑ proofread the final draft.

Overall Score _____

Writing Assessment and Portfolio Management

Writing Model

Descriptive Writing: Character Study (Theme 2, pages 192–196)

Assignment: Write a character study that uses description to bring a person to life on the page.

The Rainbow Lady

Before I moved here, I came from a small New England town where the days, the years, and even most of the people tended to blend together. But there was one woman in our town who stood out from all the rest, and her name was Vivian Esther. She stood very tall, and her silver gray hair was neatly braided, often with flowers. Her radiant complexion showed only the faintest hint of spider-like wrinkles around her eyes. We kids called her the "Rainbow Lady" because she wore dazzling green and yellow skirts, graced with cool pink and warm orange blouses. She turned out to be as kind as she was colorful.

The Rainbow Lady was best known around town as a keeper of cats—she had pet cats, stray cats, cats who were just visiting, and even cats she was asked to pet-sit. She held a special attraction for me because I loved cats and had never had one. My family often sat around our dinner table and talked about just how many cats really lived at her house.

I was soon to find out when our paths crossed early one October. She lived two blocks from us on the other side of the town green, where nearly all the houses were neat, white Victorians with black shutters, perfectly clipped lawns, and gardens that brimmed with appropriate seasonal blossoms. Her house stood on the corner lot, but it looked nothing like the neighboring Victorians. It was a crisp, yellow clapboard farmhouse with a sagging roofline. Ruby red shutters framed the glistening clean windows. The porch was filled with an array of multi-colored wicker furniture, laden with cushions and worn soft from sleeping cats.

That October day was cool and bright. As I walked by her house, I slowed down to see if I could spy her cats catching an afternoon snooze on the porch. I was so intent on trying to see the cats that I did not notice the Rainbow Lady sitting on the porch. Suddenly she stood up, dressed in several hues of green and blue, and smiled at me. "Hello," she called out, "would you like to come in for a visit?"

Identifies the subject of the character study

Describes the person's physical appearance and style of dress

Describes a scene that reveals the character's personality

Uses a variety of sentence structures

Uses an anecdote to reveal the character's personality

Writing Assessment and Portfolio Management

Well, of course I did, but I suddenly felt too shy to answer. As I walked up on the porch, I was disappointed when I didn't see any cats. The Rainbow Lady noticed the puzzled look on my face, smiled sweetly, and said, "They prefer the warmth of the parlor at this time of the day." She gently took me by the hand, and we walked into the parlor. The room was a reflection of its owner—vibrant with color and glowing in the sunlight. In contrast, on the couch were three black cats curled up together, looking almost like one. Overstuffed chairs held pairs of cats and kittens with their legs intertwined like knotted ropes. My eyes were drawn to a young orange tiger stretched out in solitude on the windowsill.

Uses effective language to make the character come alive

The Rainbow Lady moved ever so softly; I could barely hear the rustling of her skirt. She knelt and gave the tiger the softest kiss. Slowly he stirred, and she gave him a loving pet. As he stood to stretch, she picked him up and brought him over to me. My heart leaped. She sat me down, placed him gently in my lap, and patiently showed me how to pet him. I felt his contentment, and when he began to purr I looked into the Rainbow Lady's eyes.

"I think Muffin has found a new friend," she said warmly.

From then on the Rainbow Lady was more than a colorful character to me. She was Vivian, my new friend.

Concludes by summarizing the character's effect on the writer

Writing Assessment and Portfolio Management

Rubric

Narrative Writing: Short Story (Theme 3, pages 270–273)

Focus/Organization	Comments
• Includes clearly defined characters • Tells a story by developing a conflict with rising action that leads to a climax • Presents events in chronological order (and may include flashbacks) • Maintains a consistent point of view	 *Score* _____
Elaboration/Support • Describes the setting of the story with specific details • Describes the characters with specific details • Uses dialogue that sounds natural and helps to advance the plot	**Comments** *Score* _____
Grammar, Usage, and Mechanics • The story is free of misspellings. • Words are capitalized correctly. • Sentences are punctuated correctly. • Standard English usage is employed. • The paper is neat, legible, and presented in an appropriate format.	**Comments** *Score* _____

Engagement in the Writing Process   **Comments**

The student

❑ made a prewriting plan.

❑ discussed the draft with a partner.

❑ contributed questions and suggestions to other writers.

❑ revised the draft.

❑ proofread the final draft.

Overall Score _____

Writing Assessment and Portfolio Management

Writing Model
Narrative Writing: Short Story (Theme 3, pages 270–273)

Assignment: Explore the life of a fictional character by writing a short story.

The Accident

Dad was not coming out of his coma, and my older brother, Chris, was finally on his way home after staying away from us for almost a year. I stared out at the runway. It was a crystal clear night, and I saw the approaching lights of the plane long before the wheels touched the ground. I looked through eyes that burned from having shed so many tears over the last two months. I usually enjoyed watching the delicate movement of these giant birds of steel as they came back to earth, but tonight I was filled only with an empty numbness; nothing seemed real.

As people exited the plane, everyone was greeted, kissed, and hugged by someone. I stood alone and waited. Then I saw him. The tattered green backpack was slung loosely over his left shoulder. His hair, which Dad always threatened to take a pair of scissors to, was still tucked behind his ears and secured with a rubber band, but that didn't matter anymore. Dad wouldn't be able to complain this time.

Uses specific details to describe characters

Chris pretty much quit talking to me last year, the same time he quit talking to Mom and Dad. Our eyes met as he got off the plane; he didn't say anything, just gave me a quick hug with one arm. We walked silently to the baggage claim area. I couldn't tell if he was still mad at us or if he was just sad. I couldn't tell if we were brothers again. His baggage came, and we went outside to catch a taxi.

Introduces the conflict that will be resolved in the story

The words automatically spilled from my mouth, "Columbia Presbyterian Hospital." How many more times these three dreadful words were to come out of my mouth, I didn't know. All I did know was that I had been living in their echo for the better part of two months. Since my mom was always at the hospital and there was no one home to drive me, I had to call taxis back and forth to the hospital all the time. Before the accident, I had never taken one.

Chris and I rode in silence as the taxi took us across the Kingstone Bridge. As we entered downtown, Chris finally spoke to me.

Describes events in chronological order

"It's gotten worse, not better, hasn't it?" he asked.

My palms began to sweat. "I think so," I answered. "They say the machines are the only thing keeping him alive." I reached out to Chris, but he only held my hand for a minute before he suddenly released his grip. Then he buried his head in his hands and started to cry.

Uses natural-sounding dialogue to advance the plot

Writing Assessment and Portfolio Management

"I shouldn't have," he said in between sobs. I felt my eyes well up. Did he mean he shouldn't have stayed away so long, or he shouldn't have come back at all? I reached out to him again, but he ignored my hand on his shoulder. When the taxi arrived at the hospital he had quit crying, but he still wasn't looking at me or talking.

Maintains a consistent point of view

The lobby, usually full of activity, was quiet tonight. We headed to the elevator, and I pushed the second-floor button. Our ride to the Intensive Care Unit, or ICU, was on its way. In coffin-like silence we rode the elevator to the second floor.

Landing on the ICU was like arriving on another planet. We stepped out of the elevator, and I saw Chris's eyes were riveted straight ahead to the ominous sliding glass doors that welcome people to the dreadful pain of the ICU. For some reason, I turned to him and said, "Don't move. I have to show you this." I went on to explain how the entrance doors to the ICU were highly sensitive and designed to open at the slightest human approach. "But I can beat the system," I said. At first Chris stood there wearing that "what are you talking about" expression, but then he crossed his arms over his chest, cocked his head, and, for the first time that night, grinned.

Describes the setting with specific details

Uses rising action to lead to the climax

"O.K.," he said. "Prove it."

When I first figured out how to fool the doors a month ago, I thought of Chris. It was the kind of thing we used to do when we were little, when we were close. Would he think it was stupid now? As he watched, I inched my way along the wall and carefully stepped atop the gray plastic corner table strewn with magazines dating back to last Christmas. I ever so gently edged my way along the sagging fake leather couch and carefully slipped behind the five-foot palm tree. I found myself standing next to the ICU entrance doors. My heart was silently pounding, my mouth was dry, but the doors remained closed.

In silence, my eyes locked into my brother's. I was looking at a mirror image of myself. His crooked, half-bent grin burst into a full smile to match my own. Our father was still deathly ill, but I suddenly knew that whatever happened to him, I wouldn't be facing it alone. I had a brother. Chris walked toward me, the doors opened, and we walked together hand in hand into the ICU.

Ends with a climax leading to the resolution of the conflict

Writing Assessment and Portfolio Management

Rubric

Personal Narrative: Firsthand Account (Theme 4, pages 346–350)

Focus/Organization • Tells the who, what, when, where, and why of an event that the writer actually experienced • Presents events and details in a clear and logical order • Expresses personal perceptions of the event	**Comments** *Score* _____
Elaboration/Support • Uses sensory words to describe the sights, sounds, and other aspects of the event • Includes specific details to make scenes come alive	**Comments** *Score* _____
Grammar, Usage, and Mechanics • The account is free of misspellings. • Words are capitalized correctly. • Sentences are punctuated correctly, and the piece is free of fragments and run-ons. • Standard English usage is employed. • The paper is neat, legible, and presented in an appropriate format.	**Comments** *Score* _____

Engagement in the Writing Process   **Comments**

The student

❏ made a prewriting plan.

❏ discussed the draft with a partner.

❏ contributed questions and suggestions to other writers.

❏ revised the draft.

❏ proofread the final draft.   *Overall Score* _____

Writing Assessment and Portfolio Management

Writing Model

Narrative Writing: Firsthand Account (Theme 4, pages 346–350)

Assignment: Write a firsthand account of something you actually experienced.

The First Day

I lay awake in bed staring up at the ceiling, anxiously waiting for my alarm to go off. I had tossed and turned all night long and sleep was impossible. My stomach was doing flip-flops because it was the first day of school. My family had moved about a month ago, and although we had moved three times before, I still hated being the new kid. This time was different though. Not only was I starting at a new school where I didn't know anyone, it was high school and I was a freshman. They were two dreaded experiences rolled into one. I had heard so many horror stories of juniors and seniors picking on freshmen that I was scared to death.

Expresses personal perceptions of the event

The ringing of my alarm interrupted my thoughts. I threw off my covers, crawled out of bed, and stumbled into the bathroom. Every outfit I put on ended up in a heap on my floor. I had to look my best on the first day, but I was paranoid that the clothes that were cool back home wouldn't be cool here. Finally, I decided I couldn't go wrong with a T-shirt and jeans. My younger brother and sister inhaled their breakfast, but I was too nervous to eat. They had no idea what it was like to stress over high school.

Presents events in a clear order

My mom hurried the younger two outside to catch the bus and then drove me to school. During the ride, I imagined myself walking around and around the school, not finding any of my classes. I pictured a bunch of juniors and seniors knocking my books out of my hands and laughing when I bent down to pick them up. I heard my mother's comforting words of wisdom in the background as she drove, but they just came across as muffled sounds in my ears. As I got out of the car, my mom wished me luck. Thank goodness she didn't ask for a hug and kiss, since that would have been more than I could handle.

Uses sensory details to describe the event

Writing Assessment and Portfolio Management

My heart was pounding so fast I thought it was going to burst out of my chest as I climbed the stairs into the school. It was a lot bigger than my old school, but, fortunately, my homeroom turned out to be the first room along the left wall. I would have rather died than ask someone where to go. I sat silently at the desk next to the door, smelling a fresh coat of paint. Next to me and behind me, kids I didn't know chatted excitedly about their summers or their after-school plans. We were all assigned lockers, the bell jangled in my ears, and we moved on to our next class. My classes all seemed to run together, with the teachers rambling on about rules, guidelines, and requirements.

Uses specific details to make the scene come alive

The worst part of the day was lunch. Although I found my way to the cafeteria, I was mortified that I had no one to sit with. I waited in line for a bagel and iced tea. My stomach growled loudly since I had skipped breakfast, and I hoped that no one heard. I felt lost as I glanced around the lunchroom, but I managed to find an empty table and sat down. I was there by myself for what seemed like an eternity but was actually only a few minutes.

Eventually, other first-year students began to join me at my table. We were all pretty shy, but as we started to make small talk, I realized that everyone was just as unsure about this exciting, yet scary, environment as I was. I began to relax once I knew there were people sharing my own doubts and fears. While the end of the day could not come fast enough, and I still didn't really know anyone, none of the horror stories I had created in my head had come true, and I began to think that high school wasn't going to be that bad.

Tells the who, what, where, when, and why of the event

Name _____ Date _____ Class _____

Writing Assessment and Portfolio Management

Rubric

Expository Writing: Biographical Essay (Theme 5, pages 426–429)

Focus/Organization	Comments
• Clearly states a thesis • Focuses on a person and explains events or choices in the person's life • Presents information in a logical order • States an effective conclusion	Score _____
Elaboration/Support	**Comments**
• Provides details and information to support the thesis • Uses transitions effectively to show how events are related	Score _____
Grammar, Usage, and Mechanics	**Comments**
• The piece is free of misspellings. • Words are capitalized correctly. • Sentences are punctuated correctly, and the piece is free of fragments and run-ons. • Standard English usage is employed. • The paper is neat, legible, and presented in an appropriate format.	Score _____

Engagement in the Writing Process   **Comments**

The student
❑ made a prewriting plan.
❑ discussed the draft with a partner.
❑ contributed questions and suggestions to other writers.
❑ revised the draft.
❑ proofread the final draft.

*Overall Score*_____

Writing Assessment and Portfolio Management

Writing Model
Expository Writing: Biographical Essay (Theme 5, pages 426–429)

Assignment: Write a biographical essay that shows the impact that personal choices or significant events have made on someone's life.

A Step Beyond

From the death of her beloved dog to the divorce of her parents, Heather was a target for bad luck. However, she never complained or whined, "Why me?" She had been challenged by many obstacles in her life, but her positive attitude and perseverance enabled her to succeed in spite of—or perhaps even because of— these hardships. Even when she had a catastrophic accident on the ski slope, she worked hard to bounce back and make the best of her situation. In fact, she worked so hard after the accident that she ended up achieving more than ever.

States a thesis clearly

The accident happened on an unusually mild winter day in Vermont. The sun's reflection off the snow was blinding. The sky was a clear blue, with not even a cloud on the horizon. Almost everyone on the ski team had called it quits after a long day of hard training, but Heather wanted one more run. Her last slalom time had not been great, and she wanted to end with a good run. Standing at the top, she focused on the course and then sped through the starting gate. Just as she passed the halfway mark, her time looking promising, the tip of one of her new skis caught the stake of the blue gate. The sudden collision and her great momentum brought her tumbling to the ground. Only the outline of her skis and poles trailing her body could be seen sliding down the mountain under the giant spray of snow.

Focuses on events in a person's life

She had to be rushed to the hospital, where she learned that she had shattered the growth plate in her knee. Doctors informed her that she would need two major operations during the course of the next two years. Meanwhile, she would be unable to take part in any sort of strenuous physical activity, and it was doubtful she would ever downhill ski again. In one brief moment, all her hopes and dreams of being on the downhill ski team in college had been ruined. She stood on the sidelines and watched a teammate take away the state title she had wanted so much.

Writing Assessment and Portfolio Management

However, she never felt sorry for herself and refused to succumb to despair. After surgery, she fought through a great deal of pain and hardship, both emotional and physical. While she was heartbroken that she could no longer ski downhill, she worked with her physical therapist as hard as if she were training for an athletic event. She had to relearn simple things that she had always taken for granted, like how to climb stairs and how to get into and out of a chair. Many people would be frustrated and depressed under similar circumstances, but Heather approached the therapy as a challenge. In the process, she learned things about muscles, bones, and coordination that helped her when she was able to start training for a new sport—cross-country skiing. She battled to overcome what seemed insurmountable physical odds, but her dedication and perseverance finally paid off.

Presents details to support the thesis

Uses transitions effectively to show how events are related

Three years after the accident, Heather confidently glided past her opponents in the last race of the season—the state finals. She saw the finish line in the near distance and was the first one to cross it—accompanied by the well-earned applause of hundreds of fans. Some were familiar faces and others were complete strangers, but they were all cheering on the new state champion. Because of Heather's perseverance and positive attitude, she achieved as a cross-country skier the goal she hadn't been able to achieve as a downhill skier before the accident.

States an effective conclusion

Writing Assessment and Portfolio Management

Rubric

Persuasive Writing: Advice Essay (Theme 6, pages 486–490)

Focus/Organization • Begins by clearly stating a problem • Identifies the writer's qualifications for giving advice in the relevant area • States advice in a clear, convincing way • Concludes with a persuasive restatement of the advice	**Comments** *Score* _____
Elaboration/Support • Gives reasons, facts, and personal experiences to support the advice • Uses persuasive arguments and language to appeal to the reader	**Comments** *Score* _____
Grammar, Usage, and Mechanics • The essay is free of misspellings. • Words are capitalized correctly. • Sentences are punctuated correctly, and the piece is free of fragments and run-ons. • Standard English usage is employed. • The paper is neat, legible, and presented in an appropriate format.	**Comments** *Score* _____

Engagement in the Writing Process   **Comments**

The student
❑ made a prewriting plan.
❑ discussed the draft with a partner.
❑ contributed questions and suggestions to other writers.
❑ revised the draft.
❑ proofread the final draft.

Overall Score _____

Writing Assessment and Portfolio Management

Writing Model

Persuasive Writing: Advice Essay (Theme 6, pages 486–490)

Assignment: Write an advice essay, offering help to others who might benefit from your experience.

"Getting Along"

Parents and teenagers often have trouble getting along, and for a long time, my parents and I were no exception. Things have been a lot better between us this year, though. The reason is that we've each learned to try to understand where the other one is coming from, which makes it easier to compromise. I advise any parents and kids who are fighting a lot to try our approach: Identify the reasons the other person feels the way he or she does, take those into account, and then search for common ground.

Begins by clearly stating a problem

I am a good example of how well this approach works because now I get along great with my parents, but up until last year, we used to argue all the time. It seemed like we fought over everything, but the main thing we disagreed on was what clothes, equipment, and food they would buy for me. My family isn't rich, but we are a long way from being poor. I didn't understand why almost every time I wanted something, from a four-dollar box of cereal to a two-hundred-dollar piece of computer hardware, they would tell me that it was unnecessary and wasteful.

Identifies the writer's qualifications for giving advice in this area

Occasionally my parents compromised by letting me get a small or less expensive version of whatever I wanted, but this didn't stop the fights. Instead, I just thought that they were cheap and stingy. Finally, I got so frustrated that I yelled that at my father in the supermarket. Believe it or not, I actually screamed out, "Why are you always so stingy?" right in the cereal aisle. Needless to say, my father didn't appreciate that, and I got into trouble when I got home.

Cites personal experiences to support the advice

However, here's where we turned a corner: A few days later, my parents asked me to sit down with them. For the first time, they asked me in a calm and serious way why I wanted the things that I did. When they listened to my answer, they learned that not everything I asked for was just something I saw on TV. For example, I wanted a flat bed scanner for my computer because, as a future animator, I really felt I needed to learn more about how to manipulate art on the computer.

Then my parents told me a little bit about why they reacted the way they did when I asked for things. They said that before I was born, they had worked for two years in a country where people barely had enough to eat. They still volunteer at the soup kitchen every week. Being around people who couldn't

Copyright © by The McGraw-Hill Companies, Inc.

Writing Assessment and Portfolio Management

count on having even the most basic things made my parents aware of how much so many people have and waste. They said that when they heard me saying that I "needed" this or that, all they could think about was the people who *really* needed something.

After this conversation, I started to think more carefully about what I asked for, and my parents became more willing to discuss those things instead of calling me wasteful. When we reached a compromise on whether or not I could get something, we all felt better about it. More importantly, we realized that the better we understood each other on any issue we fought over, the better chance we had of getting along.

Whether you're a parent or a teenager, you can try this approach next time there's a family fight. I'm not saying you'll always get what you want or that you'll never disagree again, but if you follow my advice, each person involved will feel less angry even if things don't go his or her way. First, wait a few days until the dust has settled—don't try to have this conversation when you're still angry— then invite the other person to sit down with you. Ask that person to explain what the issue means to him or her. Then, ask that person to listen while you explain yourself. Whether or not you can arrive at a compromise right away, you're on the road to understanding. The next time you get in a similar conflict, remind the person that you understand his or her position. A few moments later, ask if he or she understands you.

The important thing is that you try to understand each other before you try to convince the other person to agree with your point of view. This can sometimes be hard to do when tempers are flying, but take it from me, because I know from my own experience, a little understanding can go a long way.

Uses persuasive language to appeal to the reader

States advice in a clear, convincing way

Concludes with a persuasive restatement of the advice

Writing Assessment and Portfolio Management

Rubric

Expository Writing: Extended Definition (Theme 7, pages 520–524)

Focus/Organization	Comments
• Introduces the word or idea to be defined • Provides both formal and personal definitions of the word • Compares and contrasts meanings of the word • Summarizes the writer's overall definition of the word	*Score* _____
Elaboration/Support • Gives examples of the word's uses • Uses vivid imagery in the definition	**Comments** *Score* _____
Grammar, Usage, and Mechanics • The piece is free of misspellings. • Words are capitalized correctly. • Sentences are punctuated correctly, and the piece is free of fragments and run-ons. • Standard English usage is employed. • The paper is neat, legible, and presented in an appropriate format.	**Comments** *Score* _____

Engagement in the Writing Process   **Comments**

The student
❑ made a prewriting plan.
❑ discussed the draft with a partner.
❑ contributed questions and suggestions to other writers.
❑ revised the draft.
❑ proofread the final draft.

Overall Score _____

Writing Assessment and Portfolio Management

Writing Model

Expository Writing: Extended Definition (Theme 7, pages 520–524)

Assignment: Write an expository essay that presents formal and personal definitions of a word.

Understanding Loyalty

What is loyalty? It's a word that's most often used in a positive sense. Most of us long for, and even expect, loyalty from our friends, families, and sweethearts, but do we always know what it means?

Introduces the word to be defined

Loyalty is defined in the dictionary as a faithfulness that one feels and displays toward a person, cause, government, or duty. In other words, when you are loyal to something, you feel strongly about it, and your actions reflect that. However, loyalty is stronger than affection, which is an emotion that is not necessarily reflected in action. It is also stronger than gallantry, which is an act of kindness or bravery that does not necessarily have an emotion attached to it. Loyalty is both a feeling and a set of behaviors.

Provides both formal and personal definitions of the word

One type of loyalty is found between people. For example, my parents, my brothers and sister, and our dog all feel loyal to one another. The same thing goes for my best friends at school. My friend is a basketball player and he and his teammates are loyal to one another. My older brother has had the same girlfriend for a year, and their loyalty to one another is sweet and romantic. I'm lucky that my parents get along so well; I can see another kind of loyalty in their relationship.

Gives examples of the word's uses

Robert Burns's poem "A Red, Red Rose," which we read in class, is a great example of the intense loyalty that a lover can feel for his sweetheart. When I read the poem, I kept thinking about how great and deep this poet's love was for his girlfriend because he promised to be loyal to her "[t]ill a' the seas gang dry, . . . [a]nd the rocks melt wi' the sun!" Although he has to go away from his love, he is so loyal that he promises to come back to her "[t]ho' it were ten thousand mile!"

Loyalty can also be felt toward concepts or ideals. We hope our president and our senators and representatives do what's right for our country, and the world has the best chance for peace if countries remain loyal to the idea of true harmony.

Whether loyalty is felt toward an individual, a group, or an abstract idea, it always provides a sense of certainty in the person who is loyal; and it always provides a source of strength to the person or group who receives the loyalty. In this way, loyalty is like a security blanket—a source of security and comfort. It is also like a suit of armor—a source of protection and assurance.

Uses vivid imagery in the definition

Writing Assessment and Portfolio Management

Of course, all of us have seen ties of loyalty break: Some close friendships end; some of my friends' parents have had to get divorced. Loyalty can also have negative consequences. During wars, people use their loyalties to a cause to justify hurting or even killing others.

However, I want to think more about when loyalty works! Because loyalty is a feeling as well as a set of behaviors, you can really trust someone who is loyal to you. A loyal person won't claim to feel one way but act another way. Loyal people sincerely connect what they do with what they feel and say. The unswerving support that comes from loyalty can occasionally cause problems if the sentiment is misdirected, but without loyalty, the human race would be a scared, lonely, and vulnerable species.

Summarizes the writer's overall definition of the word

Writing Assessment and Portfolio Management

Rubric

Creative Writing: Narrative Poem (Theme 8, pages 552–555)

Focus/Organization	Comments
• Tells a story by developing a plot with several events that lead up to a climax • Includes at least one clearly defined character • Describes the setting of the story	Score _____
Elaboration/Support • Uses sound devices such as rhythm, rhyme, alliteration, or repetition • Uses sensory words to suggest mood and atmosphere • Uses precise and vivid words, sound devices, and figurative language • Provides background information so that readers can follow the story	**Comments** Score _____
Grammar, Usage, and Mechanics • The poem is free of misspellings. • Words are capitalized correctly. • The paper is neat, legible, and presented in an appropriate format.	**Comments** Score _____

Engagement in the Writing Process   **Comments**

The student

❑ made a prewriting plan.

❑ discussed the draft with a partner.

❑ contributed questions and suggestions to other writers.

❑ revised the draft.

❑ proofread the final draft.

Overall Score_____

Writing Assessment and Portfolio Management

Writing Model

Creative Writing: Narrative Poem (Theme 8, pages 552–555)

Assignment: Write a narrative poem, telling a story about something that is important to you.

I Feel Foreign, I Feel at Home

My parents speak a different native tongue
I hear Korean in our New Jersey home
And from relatives who call from Seoul, far-away.
But I prefer English—
The only language I think I'll need.

Provides background information

I've only seen pictures of this land,
My ancestors' country.
My parents worry I will never know
Those things they cannot forget.

On my thirteenth birthday, my parents tell me
Come summer, we are going to Korea for a month.
"My home is here!" I yell.
I blow up to my room like a storm.

Tells a story by developing a plot

July comes and we go, landing at Kimpo Airport in Seoul.
The music flooding through my CD player
Is American, but the sights and sounds around me
Are distinctly Korean.
Everywhere I see Korean lettering,
Smiling Asian faces
Selling clothes, selling baby formula, selling cars.

Describes the setting of the story

I feel foreign, I feel at home.

Dad says the remains of ancient palaces
Still stand in each corner of the city.
In central Seoul, the department stores
Look like the ones we have in New Jersey.

Similar but different.
The young girls at the hotel wear white gloves with
Little hats that match their skirts.
They bow to my mother and father.

Writing Assessment and Portfolio Management

In a grocery store on a narrow side street
I see a giant container full of dried squid:
Hateful morsels, so chewy, so salty, so pungent.
My parents' favorite snack
Makes my lip curl and leaves me craving crackers.

Uses precise, vivid language

While I stroll with my mother,
Kind old women with short, permed hair
Sell Korean delicacies on the street:
Airy rice cookies, dried beans, fruit, roasted chestnuts.
I yearn for hamburgers and French fries.

My mother stops to greet a man selling fish-shaped
          cookies from a wagon.
Her eyes light up as she tells me
How much she loves these cookies,
How she ate them as a child,
How popular they are among Koreans.
For her I will try one, and with baited breath,
She watches me eat a cookie,
This fish-shaped bean-paste cookie.
"Delicious!" I exclaim.
Mother is as delighted as I am surprised, and
I suddenly realize how important it is to my parents
          that I learn to be Korean.

Uses repetition as a sound device

Gives the climax of the story

I feel foreign, I feel at home.

At Kimpo Airport, at journey's end,
Our relatives hug us and say
Come back soon!
When my aunt asks me if I liked Korea,
I tell her it is more beautiful than New Jersey!
Now my parents don't worry that I will never know
Those things they cannot forget.

We board the plane to New Jersey
And arrive at Newark Airport late at night.

I feel foreign, I feel at home.

Writing Assessment and Portfolio Management

Rubric

Expository Writing: Comparison-Contrast Essay (Theme 9, pages 700–704)

Focus/Organization	Comments
• Clearly states the main idea in a thesis statement • Presents ideas in a logical, consistent order • Concludes by restating the thesis and demonstrating how it has been proven • Uses parallel structure to present comparisons and contrasts clearly	*Score* _____
Elaboration/Support	**Comments**
• Uses transitions and relational terms effectively • Provides evidence to support comparisons and contrasts	*Score* _____
Grammar, Usage, and Mechanics	**Comments**
• The essay is free of misspellings. • Words are capitalized correctly. • Sentences are punctuated correctly, and the piece is free of fragments and run-ons. • Standard English usage is employed. • The paper is neat, legible, and presented in an appropriate format.	*Score* _____

Engagement in the Writing Process   **Comments**

The student

❏ made a prewriting plan.

❏ discussed the draft with a partner.

❏ contributed questions and suggestions to other writers.

❏ revised the draft.

❏ proofread the final draft.   *Overall Score* _____

Writing Assessment and Portfolio Management

Writing Model
Expository Writing: **Comparison-Contrast Essay** (Theme 9, pages 700–704)

Assignment: Write an essay comparing and contrasting two characters in a work of literature.

Comparing and Contrasting Romeo and Mercutio

Romeo and Mercutio, two characters in William Shakespeare's play *Romeo and Juliet*, are best friends. Like any pair of best friends, Romeo and Mercutio share differences as well as similarities. They have different attitudes toward romantic love, but they have similar attitudes about love and loyalty toward their friends and family. Shakespeare's portrayal of the friends' differences and similarities helps develop a major theme of the play—the constructive and destructive forces of love.

States the main idea in a clear thesis statement

Romeo and Mercutio have very different ideas about romantic love. From the very beginning of the play, love is Romeo's entire motivation and the source of both his happiness and his suffering. For example, before Romeo meets Juliet at the beginning of the play, he tells Mercutio about his lovesickness for a young lady named Rosaline: "Under love's heavy burden do I sink" (1.4.22). Romeo then describes the emotional pain of love: "Is love a tender thing? It is too rough, / Too rude, too boist'rous and it pricks like thorn" (1.4.25-26). In contrast, Mercutio has a more practical attitude toward romantic love. He does not believe that someone should suffer because of romantic love. Mercutio offers Romeo sensible advice: "If love be rough with you, be rough with love" (1.4.27). In matters of romance, Mercutio does not believe in playing the helpless victim.

Provides evidence to support comparisons and contrasts

Romeo and Mercutio, however, do share similar views about the powerful bond of love and loyalty between friends and family. In act 3, scene 1, the strength of their friendship is put to the test. Tybalt challenges Romeo to a duel, but Romeo refuses to fight him. Tybalt does not know that Romeo has just secretly married Juliet and thus become Tybalt's cousin. Mercutio, seeing Romeo's refusal to fight as a threat to Romeo's reputation, feels compelled to save Romeo's honor and fights Tybalt in Romeo's place. As Romeo tries to stop the duel, Tybalt stabs and kills Mercutio. Romeo declares, "My very friend, hath got this mortal hurt / In my behalf—my reputation stain'd / With Tybalt's slander . . . " (3.1.106-108). Romeo then rises to defend Mercutio's honor by slaying Tybalt. This scene shows how both Romeo and Mercutio are willing to sacrifice their lives for the sake of their friendship.

Uses transitions and relational terms effectively

Writing Assessment and Portfolio Management

The differences and similarities between Romeo's and Mercutio's attitudes toward love serve a dramatic purpose. The views and actions of these two friends help develop a major theme of the play—that love can be both a constructive and a destructive force. Out of love for Juliet, Romeo tries to end the feud between her family, the Capulets, and his family, the Montagues. Initially, he responds to Tybalt's challenge with love. When Tybalt challenges Romeo in act 3, Romeo says to him, "[I] love thee better than thou canst devise" (3.1.67). This shows that love can conquer hatred and bring about peace. However, love can also be destructive. Out of love for Romeo and loyalty to him, Mercutio insists on fighting Tybalt, but Mercutio's duel with Tybalt only intensifies the conflict between the feuding families and leads to a series of senseless deaths.

Presents ideas in a logical, consistent order

The differences and similarities between Romeo's and Mercutio's attitudes make the idea of love in Romeo and Juliet more complicated than it first appears. As one might expect in a love story, love is shown to be a powerful, wonderful thing, but love is also something that can encourage destructive behavior.

Concludes by restating the thesis

Writing Assessment and Portfolio Management

Rubric

Business Writing: Problem/Solution Report (Theme 10, pages 794–797)

Focus/Organization • Summarizes a problem and explains why it needs to be solved • Describes a solution and how it can be implemented • Identifies consequences of the solution, both positive and negative • Concludes with a summary of the problem/solution and a call to action	**Comments** *Score* _____
Elaboration/Support • Uses anecdotes or examples to illustrate points • Uses transitions to make reasoning clear	**Comments** *Score* _____
Grammar, Usage, and Mechanics • The proposal is free of misspellings. • Words are capitalized correctly. • Sentences are punctuated correctly, and the piece is free of fragments and run-ons. • Standard English usage is employed. • The paper is neat, legible, and presented in an appropriate format.	**Comments** *Score* _____

Engagement in the Writing Process   **Comments**

The student
❑ made a prewriting plan.
❑ discussed the draft with a partner.
❑ contributed questions and suggestions to other writers.
❑ revised the draft.
❑ proofread the final draft.

Overall Score _____

Writing Assessment and Portfolio Management

Writing Model

Business Writing: Problem/Solution Report (Theme 10, pages 794–797)

Assignment: Write a report summarizing a problem and giving a possible solution.

Reclaiming Our Driveway

This is the second year we have lived in this house, and this spring, just like last year, our dirt driveway was almost impassable because of the spring thaw from the surrounding hills. To put it simply, for six weeks every year our driveway is a saturated bog. This situation creates two problems. The first is that the car gets stuck in the mud on a regular basis. The second is that we that can't pave the driveway and put up a permanent basketball hoop. I have a proposal that will solve both these problems.

Summarizes a problem and explains why it needs to be solved

The reason our driveway turns to mush in the spring is that hills rise immediately behind our house. When the snow on the hills melts, water rushes toward the lower ground. It heads right to our driveway, where it rises until the dirt becomes mud. Last year, after getting our car stuck so deeply that three people were needed to push it out of the driveway, we began parking on the side of the road. We put down planks so that we could walk up the driveway to get to our front door without sinking in mud, but the planks themselves started sinking. We couldn't go anywhere without mud caking our shoes and splashing on our pants.

Uses examples to illustrate points

In order to solve this problem, we need to channel the water away from the driveway and toward the side of our property. To do this, we should dig a ditch about six feet deep and two feet wide behind the house, making sure that the ditch gets slightly deeper as it goes farther away from the house. We should add drain tiles to the bottom of the ditch. Drain tiles are pipes with holes, which will take in any accumulated water and help redirect it. Finally, we should fill the ditch with large pieces of gravel, so any water that falls on it will trickle quickly down to the drain tiles and be whisked down the hill along the new, alternative route. If the water is rerouted around our house and away from the driveway, our driveway should be drier next spring, and we should be able to pave it without worrying that water from the spring thaw will crack the pavement.

Describes a solution and how it can be implemented

Of course, if we reroute the water on our property, it might have consequences for our neighbors' property. Gravity always pulls water to lower ground, and their yards are a little bit lower than ours. If our new drainage system causes any

Identifies both positive and negative consequences of the solution

Writing Assessment and Portfolio Management

problems for other families, we should help them set up drainage systems as well. That way, everyone will be able to get their cars out of their driveways, even in March and April when driveways typically have turned into tracts of mud. Perhaps more importantly, we'll have our choice of paved driveways on which to play basketball.

Concludes with a summary of the problem/solution and a call to action

Writing Assessment and Portfolio Management

Rubric

Expository Writing: Research Report (Theme 11, pages 894–897)

Focus/Organization	**Comments**
• States the main idea in a thesis statement • Includes an introduction, a body, and a conclusion • Organizes information in an effective way • Concludes with a restatement of the thesis	 *Score* _____
Elaboration/Support	**Comments**
• Includes facts and details to support thesis • Uses quotations effectively to support the thesis • Includes a list of works cited	 *Score* _____
Grammar, Usage, and Mechanics	**Comments**
• The paper is free of misspellings. • Words are capitalized correctly. • Sentences are punctuated correctly, and the piece is free of fragments and run-ons. • Standard English usage is employed. • The paper is neat, legible, and presented in an appropriate format.	 *Score* _____

Engagement in the Writing Process   **Comments**

The student
❏ made a prewriting plan.
❏ discussed the draft with a partner.
❏ contributed questions and suggestions to other writers.
❏ revised the draft.
❏ proofread the final draft.

Overall Score _____

Writing Assessment and Portfolio Management

Writing Model

Expository Writing: Research Report (Theme 11, pages 894–897)

Assignment: Write a research report on a famous journey.

America's Betrayal and the Trail of Tears

Why would one group of people forcibly remove another group from their homeland? Could the relocated group ever recover from such a move? These questions must occur to anyone on first hearing about the forced march of the Cherokee. In 1838 Cherokee people living in Georgia were rounded up by federal troops and forced to walk eight hundred miles westward to an assigned section of Oklahoma. The Cherokee people call this sorrowful journey the "Trail Where They Cried" ("Brief"). Historians call it the "Trail of Tears." The events surrounding the Trail of Tears reveal a story of betrayal and injustice.

States the main idea in a thesis statement

The Cherokee had strong and long-standing ties to their homeland. The early Cherokee people lived as warriors, hunters, and farmers in the southern area of the Appalachian Mountains. The territory of the Cherokee covered a vast region, including the present-day state of Georgia. When European explorers arrived during the mid-1500s, the Cherokee were the largest Native American group in North America. Most European explorers recognized the Cherokee's love for the land and respect of it (Fremon 12).

Around the beginning of the nineteenth century, the Cherokee started borrowing from the culture and customs of white settlers. For example, many Cherokee began to live in log cabins, raise cattle, and farm large fields. Some grew wealthy and set up large plantations. In 1821 a leader named Sequoya developed a written alphabet for the Cherokee. Using these letters, the Cherokee learned to read and write. They published an influential newspaper called the *Cherokee Phoenix*. By 1827 the Cherokee also had written a constitution that established a republican form of government, modeled after the U.S. government, for the Cherokee Nation. The Cherokee willingly adapted to many of the white settlers' ways and showed their trust for the country's political institutions. However, conflicts over land would undermine this trust.

Includes an introduction, a body, and a conclusion

The settlers' demand for Cherokee land in Georgia arose mainly from a struggle for political control. When the Cherokee adopted their constitution, Georgians felt threatened and declared that it violated the U.S. Constitution. The governor of Georgia asked President John Quincy Adams to support this position, while the state legislature took steps to force the Cherokee out of Georgia. In addition, the discovery of gold in Georgia in 1830 drew thousands of

Writing Assessment and Portfolio Management

money-hungry settlers who were eager to make their fortunes (Fremon 56). White settlers and Southern cotton planters looked hungrily at the Cherokee Nation's rich land and pressured Cherokee leaders to exchange their traditional lands for territory in the West. However, the Cherokee resisted such demands.

In 1828, the year that Andrew Jackson was elected president of the United States, the Cherokee asked the U.S. Supreme Court to defend the rights of Native Americans in the Southeast. The state of Georgia claimed the right to make laws for the Cherokee. In response, the Cherokee claimed that federal treaties and the U.S. Constitution protected this Native American group as a self-ruling nation. In 1832 Chief Justice John Marshall sided with the Cherokee in their case against Georgia. The Supreme Court declared that Georgia's actions against the Cherokee were unconstitutional. In contrast, President Jackson sided with Georgia and vowed to defy the court ruling. Jackson reportedly said, "John Marshall has made his decision. Now let him enforce it" (Fremon 60).

Includes facts and details to support the thesis

While the Supreme Court debated the Cherokee Nation's claim to their land, Jackson persuaded his supporters in Congress to pass the Indian Removal Act of 1830. This act gave the federal government the authority to provide funds for negotiating treaties with Native Americans in the Southeast. The goal of these treaties would be to force Native Americans to move west. In 1835 the federal government persuaded a small group of Cherokee to sign the Treaty of New Echota. Under this treaty, the Cherokee were paid $5 million to exchange their lands in Georgia and Alabama for new territories in the West. Because the majority of Cherokee refused to sign the Treaty of New Echota, it was considered invalid by Cherokee law (Bealer 64). In a protest letter to the federal government and the people of the United States, a Cherokee who opposed the treaty clearly stated that the people wanted to stay on the land of their ancestors. Even former president John Quincy Adams, who was not always kind to the Cherokee when he was in office, called the treaty "infamous. . . . It brings eternal disgrace upon the country" (Fremon 71). This unfair treaty became the justification for removing the Cherokee from their homeland ("Brief").

The principal chief of the Cherokee, John Ross, appealed to the leaders in Washington, D.C., one last time. At first the new president, Martin Van Buren, agreed to let the Cherokee remain on their land for two more years, but then he changed his mind. On May 23, 1838, army troops under the command of General Winfield Scott stormed into Cherokee land. The troops invaded homes and dragged people from the fields. Thousands of Cherokee were put into stockades to wait for the long march to their new western lands ("Trail"). The Reverend James, who visited the stockades, wrote, "Many Cherokees who a few days ago were in comfortable circumstances are now victims of abject poverty. . . . It is a work of war in a time of peace" (Fremon 78). Some Cherokee escaped into the

Uses quotations effectively to support the thesis

forest during this roundup. They hid in the Smoky Mountains, which lie between North Carolina and Tennessee. A brave Cherokee named Tsali escaped into the hills after killing a soldier who was harming his wife. Later Tsali and his sons turned themselves in and were executed in return for General Scott's guarantee that the rest of the Cherokee who had escaped into the mountains could remain there.

During October and November of 1838, the brutal forced march began. The Cherokee traveled an overland route that took them through Tennessee and Kentucky, the southern tip of Illinois, through Missouri and Arkansas, and finally to Oklahoma (Fremon 79). The conditions of the eight hundred-mile journey were horrendous. A doctor who accompanied the Cherokee estimated that more than four thousand of them, or almost one fifth of the entire Cherokee population, died. Illness, dehydration, malnutrition, and extreme weather conditions all contributed to the high mortality rate. Army private John Burnett recalled, "The sufferings of the Cherokees were awful. . . . They had to sleep in the wagons and on the ground without fire. And I have known as many as twenty-two of them to die in one night of pneumonia due to ill treatment, cold, and exposure" ("Trail"). John Ross's wife, Quatie Ross, was one of the thousands who perished on the Trail of Tears (Fremon 84).

Organizes information in an effective way

The effects of the Trail of Tears on Cherokee life were devastating. The Cherokee were depleted in numbers and their cultural heritage nearly destroyed. In Oklahoma, old tensions reemerged and new ones surfaced. For example, the Cherokee who had opposed the Treaty of New Echota were still angry with those who had signed it. In fact, two of the men who had helped create the treaty were murdered by an anti-treaty group. Also, the new arrivals had to get along with another Native American group known as the Old Settlers, those who had migrated from the East as much as a generation earlier. For several years, brother was pitted against brother, and the new Cherokee land was the scene of violent conflicts. The feuding finally ended in 1846.

The descendants of the Cherokee who escaped the military roundup now number about six thousand. They have emerged as the Eastern Band of the Cherokee people. Today the Cherokee keep the memory of their ancestors' ordeal alive. Every year in Cherokee, North Carolina, a play called *Unto These Hills* is performed. This play tells the story of Tsali and the sacrifice he made so that at least a few Cherokee could remain on their true homeland (Fremon 90). In 1987, about 150 years after the forced removal of the Cherokee, Congress passed a bill designating the Trail of Tears as a National Historic Trail.

The Cherokee's claim to their land was justified and respected by many people of that time, including the chief justice of the United States and several senators. The Cherokee placed their trust in the American legal system, but that trust was

Concludes with a restatement of the thesis

betrayed. President Jackson's and President Van Buren's administrations used unfair strategies and policies to force the Cherokee from their land. The cruel treatment during the Trail of Tears is one of the saddest episodes in our nation's history. Such actions were betrayals of the democratic principles of the United States.

Works Cited

Bealer, Alex W. *Only the Names Remain*. New York: Little, 1996.

"Brief History of the Trail of Tears." *Cherokee Messenger*. The Cherokee Cultural Society of Houston. 11 Oct. 2000
    <http://www.powersource.com/cherokee/history.html>.

Fremon, David K. *The Trail of Tears*. New York: New Discovery, 1994.

"The Trail of Tears." Cherokee Publishing. 11 Oct. 2000
    <http://www.chota.com/cherokee/trail.html>.

Includes a list of works cited

Writing Assessment and Portfolio Management

Rubric

Persuasive Writing: Essay (Theme 12, pages 990–993)

Focus/Organization • Clearly states a claim • Presents a logical argument • Concludes with a call to action, if appropriate	**Comments** *Score* _____
Elaboration/Support • Provides evidence to support the claim, including fact, examples, and anecdotes, where appropriate • Uses transitions to show the logic of the claim and the reasoning process	**Comments** *Score* _____
Grammar, Usage, and Mechanics • The piece is free of misspellings. • Words are capitalized correctly. • Sentences are punctuated correctly, and the piece is free of fragments and run-ons. • Standard English usage is employed. • The paper is neat, legible, and presented in an appropriate format.	**Comments** *Score* _____

Engagement in the Writing Process

The student

❑ made a prewriting plan.

❑ discussed the draft with a partner.

❑ contributed questions and suggestions to other writers.

❑ revised the draft.

❑ proofread the final draft.

Comments

Overall Score _____

Writing Assessment and Portfolio Management

Writing Model
Persuasive Writing: Essay (Theme 12, pages 990–993)

Assignment: Write a brief persuasive essay on the theme of other worlds.

Rain Forest

People seem to enjoy speculating about what amazing discoveries might result from exploring other worlds. Researchers might find a cure for some terrible diseases! Well, you don't have to travel through deep space to find a promising but almost unknown world. There's one right here on Earth: It's called the rain forest. But unless we act to save the rain forest from destruction, we may never be able to explore its full potential.

States a claim clearly

We already know of many rain forest plants that provide substances useful in treating diseases. For example, the bark of plants called *curare lianas*, found in Latin America, contains an alkaloid used to treat diseases such as multiple sclerosis and Parkinson's disease. This same alkaloid has anesthetic qualities, making it useful in tonsillectomies, eye surgery, and other types of surgery. Madagascar's rosy periwinkle contains two important anti-tumor agents. If it weren't for wild yams from Mexico and Guatemala, we would not have cortisone, a drug used in the treatment of autoimmune disorders, inflammatory diseases, and certain cancers.

Provides evidence to support the claim

Scientists have only begun to uncover the treasures of the rain forest, yet those treasures are rapidly disappearing. The rain forests are being ravaged by the logging industry, and some old-growth forests will be completely destroyed by the early 2000s.

Uses transitions to show the reasoning process

No one would dispute the fact that the world requires wood products to satisfy expanding building needs. There are no easy solutions to the problem, but there are helpful actions we can take. One important step is to increase public awareness of the value of the rain forests and the importance of continuing to use recycled wood pulp products. But first and foremost, we must not support companies that sell lumber harvested from old-growth forests. Instead, we need to support companies that have adopted strict policies prohibiting the use of old-growth pulp and have turned their energies toward developing lumber that is certified as having been harvested in a sustainable way.

Presents a logical argument

If the destruction of the rain forests continues, it will bring about the destruction of plant life that could be a vital resource in fighting human diseases. Therefore, we must protect the rain forests by supporting the use of recycled wood-pulp products, the development of lumber that has been harvested in sustainable ways, and the pursuit of alternative sources of building materials.

Concludes with a call to action

Writing Assessment and Portfolio Management

NOTES

_____

_____

_____

_____

_____

_____

_____

_____

_____

_____

_____

_____

_____

_____

_____

_____

_____

_____

_____

_____

_____

_____

_____

_____

_____

_____

Writing Assessment and Portfolio Management

NOTES

_____

_____

_____

_____

_____

_____

_____

_____

_____

_____

_____

_____

_____

_____

_____

_____

_____

_____

_____

_____

_____

_____

_____

_____

PART TWO: PORTFOLIO MANAGEMENT

This section provides

- an introduction to portfolios

- guidelines for portfolio management

- steps for establishing and managing portfolios

- portfolio evaluation forms

An Introduction to Portfolios

A portfolio is a purposeful collection of student work that can be used to assess the student's achievement and progress. Like an artist's or photographer's professional portfolio, a student's portfolio displays a range of the person's best work and shows what the person can do.

In many literature classes, teachers have students keep their written work and review it at the end of each unit. Portfolios may also be used to review other works, such as visual art or recordings of dramatic performances.

Portfolios are particularly useful for developing a comprehensive profile of a student through the inclusion of various types of work, and for evaluating student progress from the beginning of the year to the end, and at significant checkpoints along the way.

Portfolios have often been compared to videos or movies. While a single multiple-choice test might provide an accurate snapshot of a student's achievement at a given point, a portfolio provides a video of the student's performance over a period of time.

Testimonial from a portfolio user

"I began as a well-meaning but autocratic instructional leader, and ended as a facilitator in a student-driven classroom. The writing folder began as a storage container where the writing of students was stashed and hidden, and ended as a portfolio that is both an instructional resource and focus of writing-student assessment. As I developed a portfolio method of teaching I made a profound discovery: the students and I could become partners in learning, and that learning is what we in school are always about."

— James E. Newkirk, Western Heights Middle School, Hagerstown, MD

Guidelines for Portfolio Management

- A portfolio system should be established early in the year with a clear and specific purpose, an easy management system, and clear criteria for selecting and evaluating works. For example, a portfolio intended for summative assessment at the end of a term is likely to include the student's best works in a range of categories. A portfolio intended for assessment of the student's progress each week is likely to include work from various steps in the development process.

- Portfolios can include a wide variety of student work. When deciding what to include in the portfolio, be sure to consider products, processes, and performances.

- Encourage students to reflect on the works they include in their portfolios. Many students create portfolios with a table of contents and an introduction that includes their reflections for each selected work or entry. The process of creating and sharing portfolios can provide valuable opportunities for students to set goals and evaluate their own progress.

- Students should be involved in every phase of portfolios: setting goals, deciding what should be included in the portfolio, determining criteria for evaluating portfolios, and managing the portfolios from day to day.

- Let students personalize their portfolios and take responsibility for them. Ultimately, the portfolio represents the student's work, so the student must be responsible for what it includes, how often the contents are updated, and what it looks like.

- Make sure that students have easy access to their portfolios at all times, so they may refer to earlier works, continue with current projects, and update selections frequently.

- When you evaluate portfolios, make sure that students understand what is expected of them and how their work will be judged. Having regular conferences with students is an ideal way to review their portfolios, discuss their work efforts, and evaluate their progress.

- Portfolios are excellent vehicles for encouraging self-assessment and peer assessment. Try to schedule some time during class periods for students to work alone or with a partner to make decisions about what to include in their portfolios or how to improve their works. You might also ask students to write notes explaining why they included each work or what they like about it.

- How you organize and evaluate portfolios may be determined to some extent by school, district, or state requirements. For example, a state or district might require students to submit portfolios with three specific types of writing, two best works selected by the student, and two works selected by the teacher. In that case, you would need to use this framework to plan and manage portfolios in your classroom.

Steps in Establishing and Managing Portfolios

With these guidelines and principles in mind, you might want to use the following steps to establish and manage a portfolio system for your classroom.

1. Set a purpose.

Establish a set of goals for your students and yourself.
Decide how portfolios can help meet these goals.
Consider the audience that will see the portfolio teachers, students, administrators, parents.

2. Determine what type of portfolio you will use.

Choose the type of portfolio you want to use—for example, a showcase portfolio includes the student's best works for a given marking period; a process portfolio includes work from each step in the writing process. The type of portfolio depends a great deal on the purpose established in step 1.

3. Determine what kinds of work will be included.

This step also refers back to the purpose. Portfolios may include written works, audiotapes, artworks, videotapes, works in progress, journal entries, teacher observations, peer assessments, reading logs, oral reports, and so on.

With the *Glencoe Literature* program, your portfolios might include the following:

- **Responding to Literature activities and tasks**
- **Selection Tests**
- **Open-Book Theme Tests**
- **Writing Workshops**
- **Performance Assessments**
- **Theme Projects**

4. Establish procedures for collecting, organizing, and managing student works.

These are "housekeeping" details—deciding where to keep the portfolios, what to keep them in, when students will have access to their portfolios, how often you will look at them, and so on. These decisions will help determine the success of the portfolio system.

5. Establish criteria and procedures for evaluating the portfolio.

Decide how the portfolios will be assessed and who will assess them. Based on what will be included in the portfolio, you should have a set of criteria for evaluating each work in particular and all the works as a whole. You should also consider the use of self-assessment, peer review procedures, and student-teacher conferences to discuss evaluations.

Regardless of what kind of system you develop for your classroom, do not hesitate to make changes along the way. Portfolios are a dynamic form of assessment, and you may want or need to make changes in the process to ensure that they are as effective as they can be.

Writing Assessment and Portfolio Management

Portfolio Evaluation Forms

The forms on pages 59 and 60 may be used for evaluating portfolios. The **Portfolio Checklist** on page 59 can be used by you as well as by students to make sure that the portfolio includes what it is supposed to include. This form may be adapted for your classroom. The **Portfolio Evaluation Form** on page 60 can help you structure the evaluation process. It includes space for any additional criteria you might choose to add.

Determining Grades. These two forms can also be useful in helping to determine students' grades through the use of portfolios. For example, you might want to assign weighted scores to the works included in a portfolio (listed on the Checklist) and calculate a total score from the **Portfolio Evaluation Form** to serve as the basis for an overall grade.

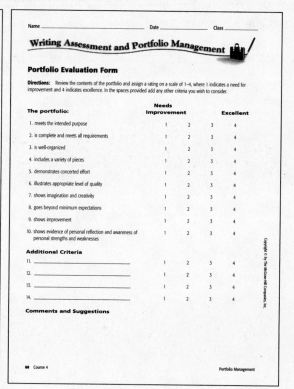

Name _____ Date _____ Class _____

Portfolio Checklist

Directions: Use this form to keep track of the contents included in the portfolio for each category. The student may clip this form to the portfolio and fill in the left column; the teacher may record dates and comments in the columns on the right.

Contents	Date	Comments
1. Student's Writing		
2. Projects		
3. Performance Tasks		
4. Classroom Activities		
5. Listening, Speaking, Viewing		
6. Tests		

Portfolio Management

Course 4 **59**

Name _____ Date _____ Class _____

Writing Assessment and Portfolio Management

Portfolio Evaluation Form

Directions: Review the contents of the portfolio and assign a rating on a scale of 1–4, where 1 indicates a need for improvement and 4 indicates excellence. In the spaces provided add any other criteria you wish to consider.

The portfolio:	Needs Improvement			Excellent
1. meets the intended purpose	1	2	3	4
2. is complete and meets all requirements	1	2	3	4
3. is well-organized	1	2	3	4
4. includes a variety of pieces	1	2	3	4
5. demonstrates concerted effort	1	2	3	4
6. illustrates appropriate level of quality	1	2	3	4
7. shows imagination and creativity	1	2	3	4
8. goes beyond minimum expectations	1	2	3	4
9. shows improvement	1	2	3	4
10. shows evidence of personal reflection and awareness of personal strengths and weaknesses	1	2	3	4

Additional Criteria

11. _____	1	2	3	4
12. _____	1	2	3	4
13. _____	1	2	3	4
14. _____	1	2	3	4

Comments and Suggestions

60 Course 4

Portfolio Management

Portfolio Checklist

Directions: Use this form to keep track of the contents included in the portfolio for each category. The student may clip this form to the portfolio and fill in the left column; the teacher may record dates and comments in the columns on the right.

Contents	Date	Comments
1. Student's Writing		
2. Projects		
3. Performance Tasks		
4. Classroom Activities		
5. Listening, Speaking, Viewing		
6. Tests		

Writing Assessment and Portfolio Management

Portfolio Evaluation Form

Directions: Review the contents of the portfolio and assign a rating on a scale of 1–4, where 1 indicates a need for improvement and 4 indicates excellence. In the spaces provided add any other criteria you wish to consider.

The portfolio:	Needs Improvement			Excellent
1. meets the intended purpose	1	2	3	4
2. is complete and meets all requirements	1	2	3	4
3. is well-organized	1	2	3	4
4. includes a variety of pieces	1	2	3	4
5. demonstrates concerted effort	1	2	3	4
6. illustrates appropriate level of quality	1	2	3	4
7. shows imagination and creativity	1	2	3	4
8. goes beyond minimum expectations	1	2	3	4
9. shows improvement	1	2	3	4
10. shows evidence of personal reflection and awareness of personal strengths and weaknesses	1	2	3	4

Additional Criteria

11. _____	1	2	3	4
12. _____	1	2	3	4
13. _____	1	2	3	4
14. _____	1	2	3	4

Comments and Suggestions

Writing Assessment and Portfolio Management

NOTES

_____
_____
_____
_____
_____
_____
_____
_____
_____
_____
_____
_____
_____
_____
_____
_____
_____
_____
_____
_____
_____
_____
_____
_____
_____
_____
_____

Name _____ Date _____ Class _____

Writing Assessment and Portfolio Management

NOTES

_____

_____

_____

_____

_____

_____

_____

_____

_____

_____

_____

_____

_____

_____

_____

_____

_____

_____

_____

_____

_____

_____

_____

Writing Assessment and Portfolio Management

NOTES

_____

_____

_____

_____

_____

_____

_____

_____

_____

_____

_____

_____

_____

_____

_____

_____

_____

_____

_____

_____

_____

_____

_____

_____

Writing Assessment and Portfolio Management

NOTES

_____
_____
_____
_____
_____
_____
_____
_____
_____
_____
_____
_____
_____
_____
_____
_____
_____
_____
_____
_____
_____
_____
_____
_____

Writing Assessment and Portfolio Management

NOTES

_____

_____

_____

_____

_____

_____

_____

_____

_____

_____

_____

_____

_____

_____

_____

_____

_____

_____

_____

_____

_____

_____

_____

_____

_____

_____

_____

_____

Writing Assessment and Portfolio Management

NOTES

_____
_____
_____
_____
_____
_____
_____
_____
_____
_____
_____
_____
_____
_____
_____
_____
_____
_____
_____
_____
_____
_____
_____
_____
_____
_____